It's another Quality Book from CGP

This book is for anyone doing AQA GCSE Graphic Products.

It contains lots of tricky questions just like the ones that could come up in the exam. They're designed to make you sweat — because that's the only way you'll get any better.

It's also got a few daft bits in to try and make the whole experience at least vaguely entertaining for you.

What CGP is all about

Our sole aim here at CGP is to produce the highest quality books — carefully written, immaculately presented and dangerously close to being funny.

Then we work our socks off to get them out to you — at the cheapest possible prices.

Contents

SECTION ONE — THE DESIGN PROCESS

SECTION TWO — MATERIALS AND COMPONENTS

SECTION THREE — GRAPHICAL TECHNIQUES

SECTION FOUR — TYPES OF DRAWINGS

SECTION FIVE — SOCIETY AND THE ENVIRONMENT

SECTION SIX — SYSTEMS AND INDUSTRY

Published by CGP

Editors:
Katherine Craig, Ben Fletcher, Sarah Hilton, Delene Kang, Adam Moorhouse, Caley Simpson.

Contributors:
Catherine Atsiaris, Janice Donoghue, Debbie McGrory.

With thanks to Ryan Ball for the content review.
With thanks to Sharon Keeley and Adrian Lee for the proofreading.

With thanks to Laura Stoney for the copyright research.

ISBN: 978 1 84762 392 8

Clipart from Corel®

With thanks to iStockphoto® for permission to use the lemon squeezer image on page 8.

With thanks to Valpak for permission to reproduce the Green Dot® symbol on page 45.

With thanks to The British Toy & Hobby Association for permission to reproduce the Lion Mark logo on page 50.

Printed by Elanders Ltd, Newcastle upon Tyne.

Based on the classic CGP style created by Richard Parsons.

Exam Advice

The Exam Paper is in Two Sections

1) There's just <u>one exam</u> for AQA Graphics, but it's split into <u>two sections</u> — Section A and Section B.

2) You need to answer <u>all of the questions</u> in both sections.

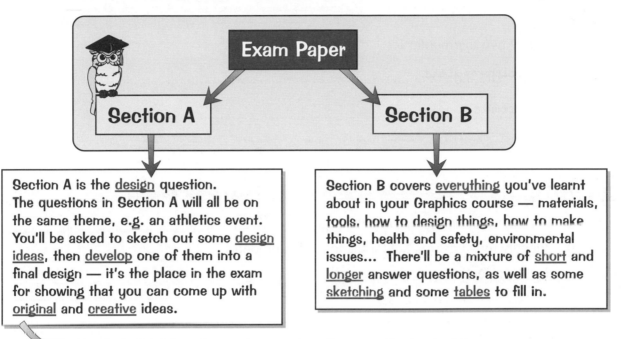

Section A is the <u>design</u> question. The questions in Section A will all be on the same theme, e.g. an athletics event. You'll be asked to sketch out some <u>design ideas</u>, then <u>develop</u> one of them into a final design — it's the place in the exam for showing that you can come up with <u>original</u> and <u>creative</u> ideas.

Section B covers <u>everything</u> you've learnt about in your Graphics course — materials, tools, how to design things, how to make things, health and safety, environmental issues... There'll be a mixture of <u>short</u> and <u>longer</u> answer questions, as well as some <u>sketching</u> and some <u>tables</u> to fill in.

A little while before the exam, your teacher will give you a <u>Preparation Sheet</u>. This gives you the <u>theme</u> of the Section A question — use it to do some <u>research</u>.

3) The exam lasts for <u>2 hours</u>. Each question will have a suggestion of how long you should spend on it. Try to follow this — it really will help you to have a good go at every question.

4) One of your answers will be assessed for <u>quality of written communication</u> — that's spelling, punctuation and grammar, as well as how clear your answer is. You'll be <u>told</u> which question this is on the front of the exam paper — so read all that information carefully and put a <u>note</u> to yourself next to the relevant question.

There are a Few Golden Rules

1) Always, always, always make sure you <u>read the question</u> properly. For example, if the question asks you to sketch <u>three</u> design ideas, make sure you do three — <u>not two, not four</u>. And don't <u>waste loads of time</u> making them really neat — they're only supposed to be sketches. *(There are places where you do need to be really neat though — drawing graphs and charts, or a final design idea.)*

2) And while we're on the subject of sketches — the examiners will often ask you to <u>annotate</u> them. This <u>doesn't</u> just mean add labels — you need to <u>explain</u> your <u>ideas</u> fully.

3) It's a good idea to <u>underline</u> the important bits of the question. Then you can keep checking to make sure you're not going off track and waffling about stuff that's not going to get you any marks.

4) Pay attention to the <u>number of marks</u> a question is worth — if it's worth three marks, give three good points. And try to <u>fill</u> most of the space available for the answer. If there are three lines and you've only filled one, you probably haven't written enough.

5) Always use the right <u>technical words</u> — words like 'typeface' and 'pictogram' make examiners happy.

6) Make your answers as <u>specific</u> as possible. If you're asked to suggest a material, don't just write plastic — give a specific type of plastic.

Exam Advice

You Need to Understand the Command Words

Command words are the words in a question that tell you what to do — describe, explain, etc.
If you don't know what they mean, you won't be able to answer the questions properly. Boo hoo.

Name...

If you're asked to name something just say what it's called — you don't need to give any extra information.

6   **a)**   Name two thermoplastics.

1. _polypropylene_ ....

2. _acetate_ ....

(2 marks)

Identify...

You just need to write down the answer — you don't need to explain it.

2   A designer is doing some market research.

  a)   Identify the target market for the following products.

    i)   A poster advertising a new doll.

parents of young girls ....

(1 mark)

Describe...

Describing means picking out the features — of, say, an object or a process. If you're asked to just 'briefly describe' something you don't need to go into too much detail.

4   Die cutting is used to produce the nets for cardboard packaging.

  a)   Describe the process of die cutting.

Sharp blades for cutting are bent into the right shape so that they match the

outline of the net. These are then mounted on to a base. Rounded blades for

creasing are added to the base. These are then pressed down into the card.

(3 marks)

Explain...

If you're asked to explain something, you need to give reasons — don't just write out what it is.

3   **b)**   Explain why lithography is an appropriate method for printing
5000 copies of a fashion magazine.

Lithography is a very fast printing process, so it won't take long to print

all of the magazines. It also produces a high quality product, so photos in

the magazine will print clearly.

(2 marks)

Exam Advice

Evaluate...

You need to weigh something up — here you need to compare your idea to the specification and decide whether you've covered each point.

1 b) A design specification for a children's book has the following points:

- The book must be suitable for a young child.
- The book must be made from environmentally friendly material.

Evaluate your design idea against the design specification above.

The bright colours will appeal to children, and the large font size will make it easy for them to read. The book will be made from recycled paper so it will be environmentally friendly, as trees won't need to be felled to make new paper.

(4 marks)

Analyse...

Analysing is <u>picking out</u> and <u>evaluating</u> the features of something. Here you'd have to say whether each feature of the catalogue makes it suitable for its target market.

7 Analyse this design idea for a fashion catalogue cover. The catalogue is aimed at older women. Comment on whether you think the design is suitable for its target market.

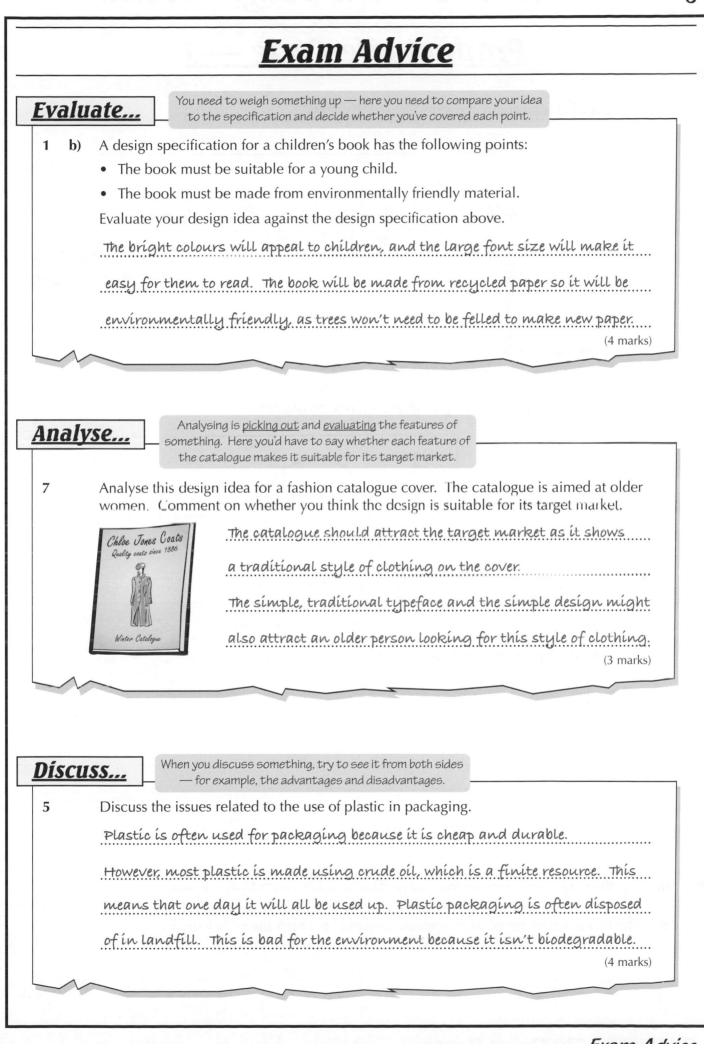

Chloe Jones Coats
Quality coats since 1886

Winter Catalogue

The catalogue should attract the target market as it shows a traditional style of clothing on the cover.

The simple, traditional typeface and the simple design might also attract an older person looking for this style of clothing.

(3 marks)

Discuss...

When you discuss something, try to see it from both sides — for example, the advantages and disadvantages.

5 Discuss the issues related to the use of plastic in packaging.

Plastic is often used for packaging because it is cheap and durable. However, most plastic is made using crude oil, which is a finite resource. This means that one day it will all be used up. Plastic packaging is often disposed of in landfill. This is bad for the environment because it isn't biodegradable.

(4 marks)

Product Life-Cycle — 1

1 Explain what is meant by the term 'gap in the market'.

....

(1 mark)

2 Suggest a suitable **target market** for the leather-bound diary shown in **Figure 1**.

Figure 1

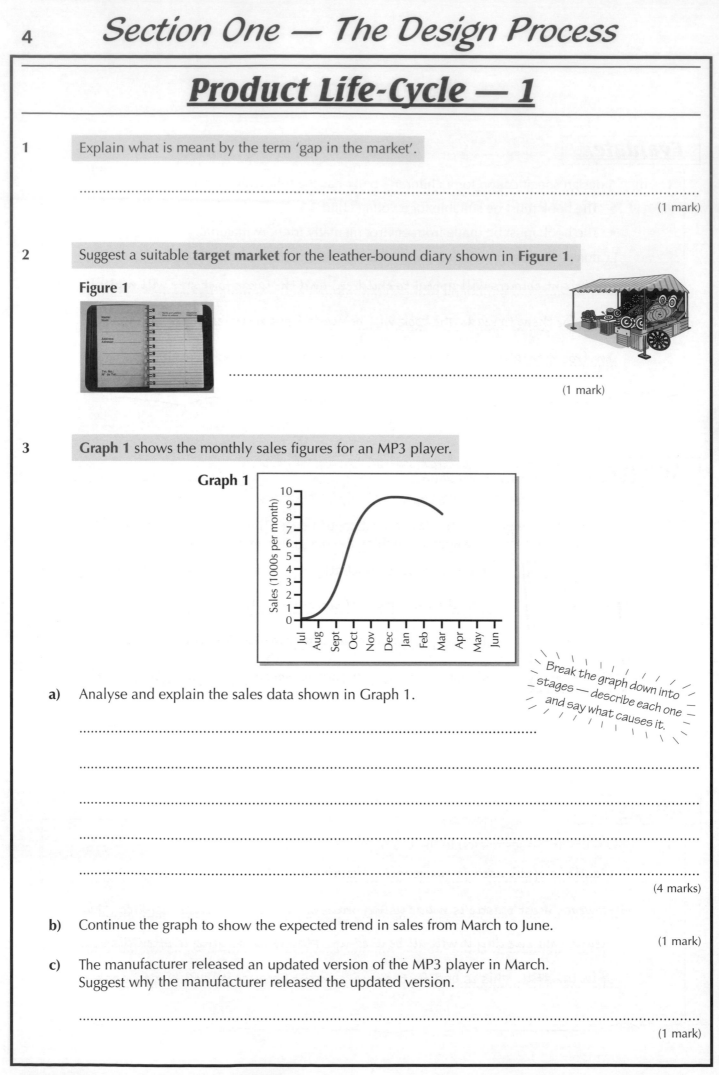

....

(1 mark)

3 **Graph 1** shows the monthly sales figures for an MP3 player.

Graph 1

Break the graph down into stages — describe each one and say what causes it.

a) Analyse and explain the sales data shown in Graph 1.

....

....

....

....

....

(4 marks)

b) Continue the graph to show the expected trend in sales from March to June.

(1 mark)

c) The manufacturer released an updated version of the MP3 player in March.
Suggest why the manufacturer released the updated version.

....

(1 mark)

Product Life-Cycle — 2

4   Many products are designed with **planned obsolescence**.

'Planned obsolescence' is the same thing as 'built-in obsolescence'.

a)   Explain what is meant by the term 'planned obsolescence'.

....

(1 mark)

b)   Explain the advantages and disadvantages of planned obsolescence.

   i)   The advantages of planned obsolescence are...

   ....

   ....

(2 marks)

   ii)   The disadvantages of planned obsolescence are...

   ....

   ....

(2 marks)

c)   A new range of stationery is being designed, which includes the ring-binder shown in **Figure 2**. Describe **two** ways that designers could build obsolescence into the design of the ring-binder.

Figure 2

....

....

....

(2 marks)

5   **Figure 3** shows a stand-up menu designed for a new cafe.

Figure 3

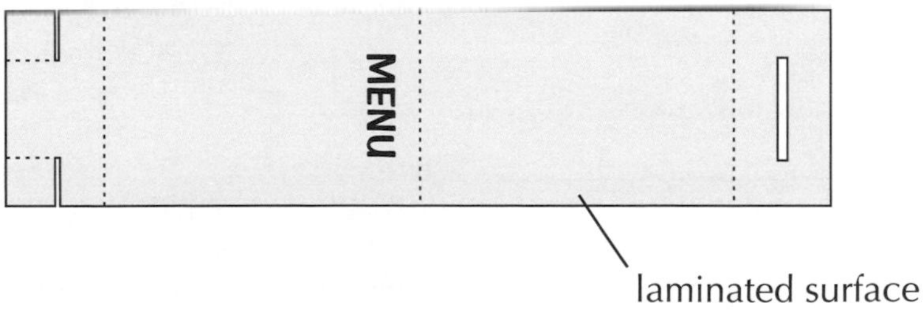

laminated surface

Explain how the menu has been designed for maintenance.

....

....

....

(2 marks)

Product Analysis — 1

1   Explain the difference between **quality of design** and **quality of manufacture**.

....

....

(2 marks)

2   A kitchen equipment company plans to design a new kettle.
Figure 1 shows two **existing products**.

Figure 1

Product 1   Product 2

a)   Give **one** reason why designers should analyse existing products before designing a new product.

....

(1 mark)

b)   Evaluate the two products shown in **Figure 1**. Comment on:

    i)   how well they meet customers' needs

       ....

       ....

       ....

(2 marks)

    ii)   their appearance

There's no right or wrong answer for this — you just need to say what you think about the appearance of the two kettles.

       ....

       ....

       ....

(2 marks)

c)   State one change you could make to the design of either product,
and say why it is an improvement.

Product: ....

Modification: ....

Why it is an improvement: ....

(2 marks)

Product Analysis — 2

3   A new measuring jug is being designed.
The designers need to collect some **anthropometric data**.

a)   Explain what is meant by 'anthropometric data'.

....
(1 mark)

b)   Give **one** piece of anthropometric data that would be needed by the designers.

....
(1 mark)

c)   Assess the suitability of clear polypropylene as a material for the measuring jug.

....

....
(2 marks)

4   A design for an alphabet book for **young children** is shown in **Figure 2**.

Figure 2

Give **two** ergonomic issues that should be considered when designing books for young children.

....

....

....
(2 marks)

5   **Figure 3** shows a design for a new headset.
Table 1 shows average measurements collected from a sample of adults.

Figure 3

Table 1

Length of foot	205 mm
Width of head	148 mm
Distance between elbow and shoulder	285 mm
Distance between ear and mouth	128 mm
Distance between eyes	42 mm

Using **Table 1**, suggest what measurements should be used for dimensions **a** and **b** in **Figure 3**.

a)   .... mm
(1 mark)

b)   .... mm
(1 mark)

Designers and What They Do

1   Name the designer of the product shown in **Figure 1**.

Figure 1

....

(1 mark)

2   Jock Kinneir and Margaret Calvert are well-known designers.

a)   Name one design project for which Kinneir and Calvert are well known.

....

(1 mark)

b)   Briefly explain why Kinneir and Calvert's design for this project was so effective.

....

....

(2 marks)

c)   Redesign the graphic in **Figure 2** in Kinneir and Calvert's style.
Use notes to describe the changes you have made.

Figure 2

GRAPHICS
IS
GREAT

(4 marks)

3   In 1933, a designer produced a simplified map of the London Underground system.

a)   Name the designer of this simplified map.

....

(1 mark)

b)   Explain why the design of the map was so effective.

....

....

....

(3 marks)

<u>Design Briefs and Specifications — 1</u>

1 Write a **design brief** for a product that will advertise a new chocolate bar, shown in **Figure 1**.

Figure 1

Figure 1

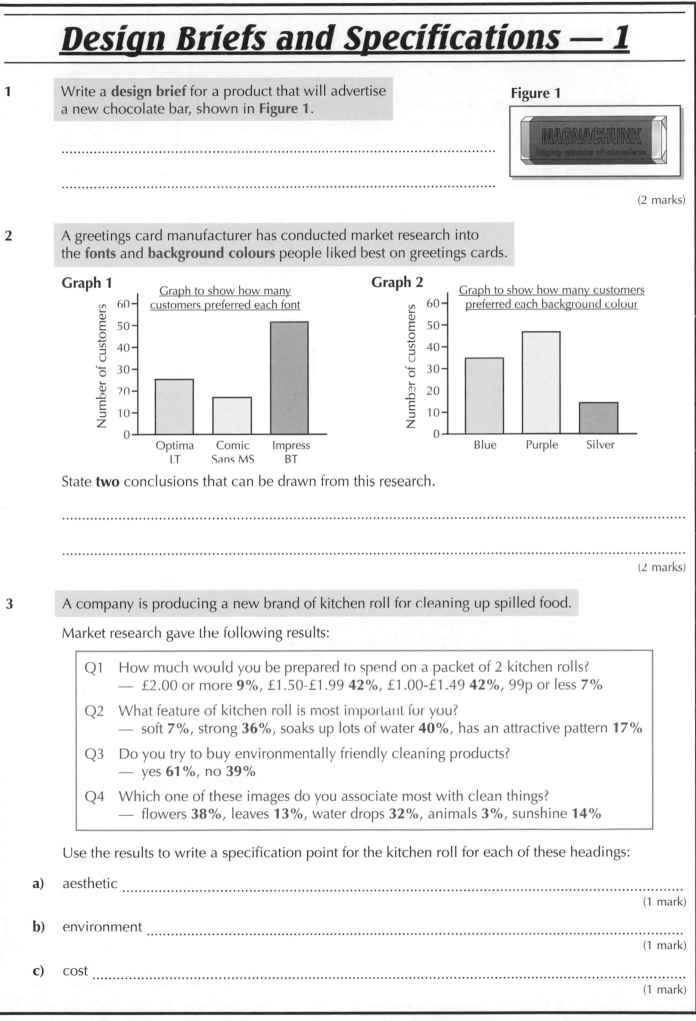

....

....

(2 marks)

2 A greetings card manufacturer has conducted market research into the **fonts** and **background colours** people liked best on greetings cards.

Graph 1

Graph to show how many customers preferred each font

Number of customers

60 50 40 30 20 10 0

Optima LT | Comic Sans MS | Impress BT

Graph 2

Graph to show how many customers preferred each background colour

Number of customers

60 50 40 30 20 10 0

Blue | Purple | Silver

State **two** conclusions that can be drawn from this research.

....

....

(2 marks)

3 A company is producing a new brand of kitchen roll for cleaning up spilled food.

Market research gave the following results:

> Q1 How much would you be prepared to spend on a packet of 2 kitchen rolls?
> — £2.00 or more **9%**, £1.50-£1.99 **42%**, £1.00-£1.49 **42%**, 99p or less **7%**
>
> Q2 What feature of kitchen roll is most important for you?
> — soft **7%**, strong **36%**, soaks up lots of water **40%**, has an attractive pattern **17%**
>
> Q3 Do you try to buy environmentally friendly cleaning products?
> — yes **61%**, no **39%**
>
> Q4 Which one of these images do you associate most with clean things?
> — flowers **38%**, leaves **13%**, water drops **32%**, animals **3%**, sunshine **14%**

Use the results to write a specification point for the kitchen roll for each of these headings:

a) aesthetic ....

(1 mark)

b) environment ....

(1 mark)

c) cost ....

(1 mark)

10

Design Briefs and Specifications — 2

4 This question is about designing. The brief is to design a **logo** for the new children's cereal bar 'Fruity Loopy'. The specification for the logo is shown in **Figure 1**.

Figure 1

The logo should:
- give the name
- indicate the flavour
- have a health theme
- appeal to children

Sketch **two** ideas for the logo in the space below.
Include notes in your sketches.

(6 marks)

5 'Greenways' is a transport company that delivers goods using methods that create as little pollution as possible.

Sketch with notes a design for the **logo** that will go on all the company's vehicles.

(4 marks)

Section 1 — The Design Process

Development and Evaluation — 1

1 Models, mock-ups and prototypes are used in the development and evaluation stages of design.

Explain what is meant by a:

a) scale model ....

....

(1 mark)

b) mock-up ....

....

(1 mark)

c) prototype ....

....

(1 mark)

2 Explain why CAD can be useful when designers are modelling their ideas.

....

(1 mark)

3 A designer has made a prototype of a label for a shampoo bottle.
Figure 1 shows the specification. **Figure 2** shows the prototype.

Figure 1
The label should:
* show the name of the product and what it smells of
* have a futuristic or scientific appearance
* include an image of glossy hair
* last until the shampoo bottle is empty under normal use

Figure 2

a) Evaluate the prototype design against the specification.

....

....

....

....

(4 marks)

b) Suggest what **tests** the designer should carry out on the prototype label
to check whether it is fit for purpose.

....

....

(2 marks)

<u>Development and Evaluation — 2</u>

4 This question is about designing a box to carry hot takeaway pizza.

Figure 3 shows an initial design idea.

Figure 3

MAMA'S PIZZA

a) In the space below, develop the design for the box.
Marks will be awarded for choice of materials, construction details and graphics.

> You don't just need to add to what's there — you could make adjustments to the shape too.

(7 marks)

b) Evaluate your design and explain how it is an improvement on **Figure 3**.

....

....

....

....

(4 marks)

Manufacturing Specification

1   A Christmas card design has a Christmas tree hanging in a window. **Figure 1** shows the tools and components needed. **Figure 2** shows the inside and front of a finished card.

Figure 1

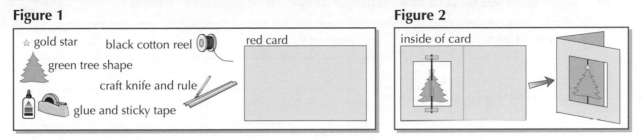

Figure 2

Show the assembly process as a flow chart.

Start →

Flow charts can run across or down the page.

(3 marks)

2   **Figure 3** shows a storage box. **Figure 4** shows the manufacturing process for making one box.

Figure 3

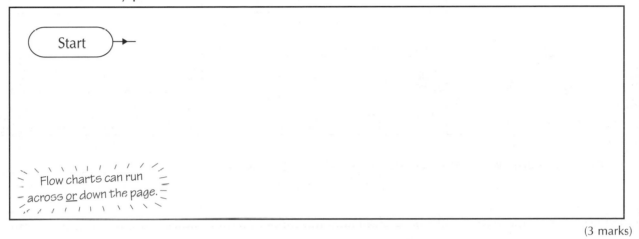

Figure 4

	5 min	10 min	15 min	20 min	25 min	30 min	35 min	40 min	45 min	50 min	55 min	60 min	65 min	70 min	75 min	80 min	85 min
Mark out surface development	■	■	■														
Cut out the box and lid				■													
Paint the box					■	■											
Allow the paint to dry							■	■	■								
Paint the lid										■							
Allow the paint to dry											■	■	■				
Apply the labels to the lid														■			
Assemble the box and lid																■	■

Explain **one change** that could be made to the manufacturing process to reduce the total time it takes.

....

(1 mark)

Paper and Board — 1

1 There are lots of **different types of paper** that are used for different jobs.

a) In the table below, state **one** property and **one** use of each type of paper.

Type of paper	Property	Use
Layout paper	....	....
Cartridge paper	....	....
Bleed-proof paper	....	....

(6 marks)

b) A designer wants to make a copy of a drawing by hand.

   i) Suggest which type of paper he should use.

   ....

(1 mark)

   ii) Explain why this type of paper is the most suitable.

   ....

(1 mark)

2 Paper can be bought in a variety of sizes.

a) State the **size** of paper that matches the descriptions below.

   i) Half the size of A5: ....

(1 mark)

   ii) Double the size of A3: ....

(1 mark)

b) A sheet of paper is described as 100 gsm. Explain what gsm means.

....

....

(2 marks)

3 Explain why paper and board are often quite **sustainable materials**.

....

....

(2 marks)

Paper and Board — 2

4   Suggest a suitable board for each product below, and explain your suggestions.

a)   Box to store products in a warehouse

Type of board: ....

Explanation: ....

....

....

(3 marks)

b)   Chocolate box

Type of board: ....

Explanation: ....

....

....

(3 marks)

c)   Board surrounding a painting

Type of board: ....

Explanation: ....

....

....

(3 marks)

5   **Laminating** paper with another material can change its properties.

a)   Suggest a use for paper laminated with aluminium and explain your answer.

....

....

(2 marks)

b)   Give a material that could be used to laminate paper to make paper cups. Explain your answer.

....

....

(2 marks)

c)   Suggest why laminated paper can be hard to recycle.

....

(1 mark)

Paper and Board — 3

6   Different types of paper and board are suitable for different products.

   a)   State a property that paper used for certificates should have.

      ....

                            (1 mark)

   b)   **i)**   Suggest a suitable type of laminated board for modelling 3D products.

          ....

                               (1 mark)

       ii)   Describe the properties of this type of board that make it suitable for this use.

          ....

                              (2 marks)

7   This question is about spiral wound tubes.

   a)   Describe how spiral wound tubes are made.

      ....

      ....

                               (2 marks)

   b)   Give **one** use of spiral wound tubes.

      ....

                               (1 mark)

8   Give **one** advantage and **one** disadvantage of using the materials below to package food products.

   a)   Solid white board

      i)   Advantage: ....

                                (1 mark)

      ii)   Disadvantage: ....

                                (1 mark)

   b)   Recycled grey board laminated with high-quality paper

      i)   Advantage: ....

                                (1 mark)

      ii)   Disadvantage: ....

                                (1 mark)

   c)   Corrugated cardboard

      i)   Advantage: ....

                                (1 mark)

      ii)   Disadvantage: ....

                                (1 mark)

Plastics — 1

1   For each product below, **circle** the most suitable plastic to make it from. **Explain** each choice.

a)   Insulation for electrical wires

PVC	expanded polystyrene

This plastic is most suitable because:

Give a useful property of the plastic you choose and a drawback of the other plastic.

....

....

....

(2 marks)

b)   Plastic wallets for holding documents

polypropylene	high-impact polystyrene

This plastic is most suitable because:

....

....

....

(2 marks)

c)   Windows in packaging that allow a product to be seen.

acetate	corrugated plastic sheet

This plastic is most suitable because:

....

....

....

(2 marks)

2   Many plastics are not very **sustainable**.

Explain why this is.

....

....

(2 marks)

Plastics — 2

3   This question is about plastics.

a)   Suggest a plastic that would be suitable for making each of the following products.
Give **one** reason for each suggestion.

i)

Suitable plastic: ....

Reason: ....

....

(2 marks)

ii)

Suitable plastic: ....

Reason: ....

....

(2 marks)

iii)

Suitable plastic: ....

Reason: ....

....

(2 marks)

b)   Explain what a thermoplastic is.

....

(1 mark)

4   Some plastics are useful as **modelling materials**.

a)   Describe the properties of expanded polystyrene that make it a good modelling material.

....

....

(2 marks)

b)   Describe the properties of machining foam that make it a good modelling material.

....

....

(2 marks)

c)   Describe the properties of corrugated plastic sheet that make it a good modelling material.

....

....

(2 marks)

Section 2 — Materials and Components

Modern and Smart Materials

1 Some modern **packaging** materials are made from **plant products**.

a) Name **one** of these materials, and state what it is made from and what it is used for.

Name: ....

Made from: ....

Use: ....

(3 marks)

b) Explain why packaging materials made from plants are considered to be environmentally friendly.

....

....

(2 marks)

2 Jewellery can be made from **precious metal clay**.
Describe, using notes and sketches, how you would make a ring from precious metal clay.

(4 marks)

3 An electronics company is designing a warning patch that uses a **smart material** to show when a microchip begins to overheat.

a) Briefly describe what smart materials are.

....

....

(2 marks)

b) Suggest and describe a smart material that the company could use.

....

....

(2 marks)

Fillers and Finishing

1   Figure 1 shows a prototype note holder made using balsa wood and acrylic.
     The prototype will be finished with a painted surface.

Figure 1

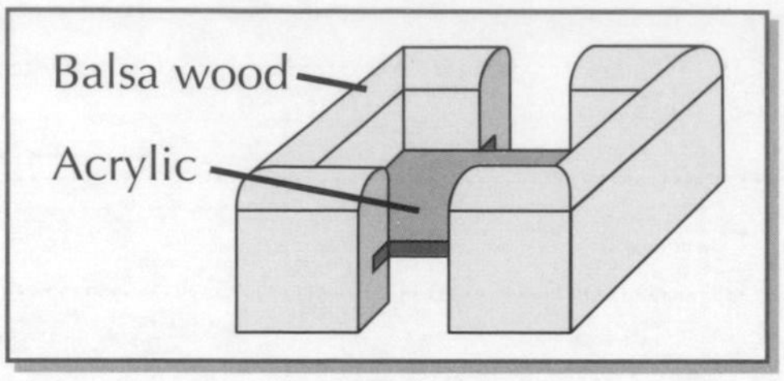

Balsa wood
Acrylic

a)   Describe how you would prepare the surface of the balsa wood for finishing.

     ....

     ....

     ....

     ....
                                                                                                                              (4 marks)

b)   Describe the stages of painting the surface of the balsa wood.

     ....

     ....

     ....
                                                                                                                              (3 marks)

2   A new restaurant menu with a high-quality look is to be printed.
     Table 1 shows the surface finishes that could be used.

Table 1

| Laminating (encapsulation) |
| Varnishing |
| Embossing |
| Foil application |

Select **one** finish you would use for the menu.

I would use ....

Explain why this surface finish is appropriate for the menu.

You don't get a mark for choosing a finish — both marks come from your explanation.

     ....

     ....
                                                                                                                              (2 marks)

Section 2 — Materials and Components

<u>Drawing and Painting</u>

1   Name each graphical tool in **Table 1** and explain how it is **used**.

Make sure you give precise names.

Table 1

Tool	Name	Use
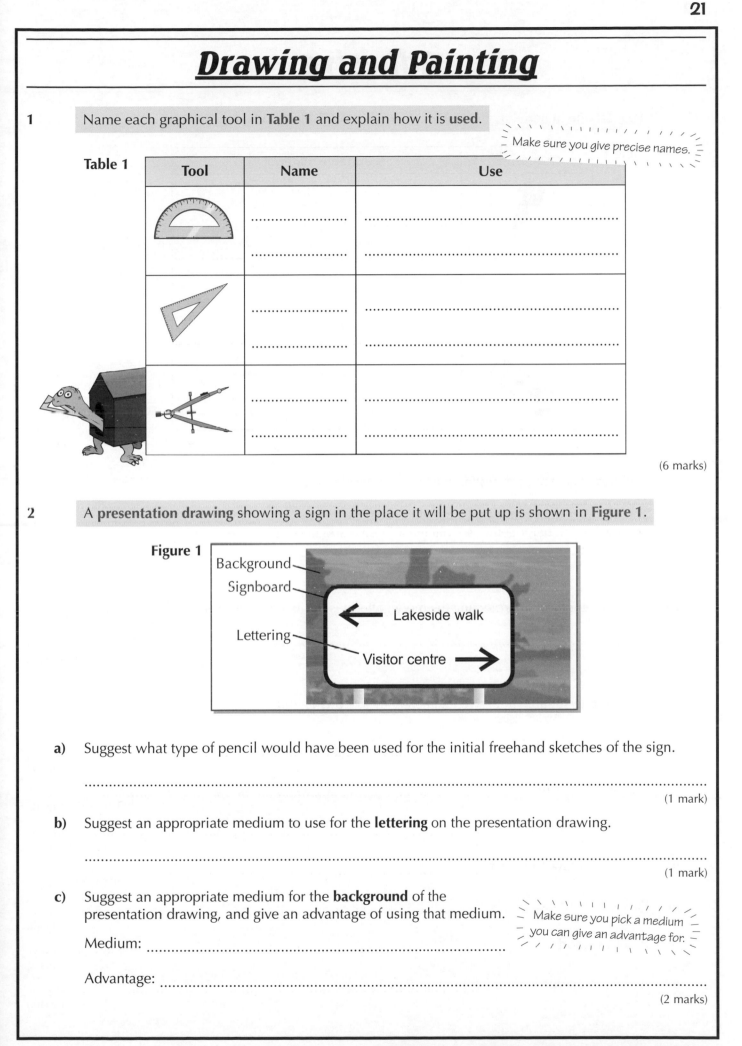	....	....
	....	....
	....	....

(6 marks)

2   A **presentation drawing** showing a sign in the place it will be put up is shown in **Figure 1**.

Figure 1

Background
Signboard
Lettering
Lakeside walk
Visitor centre

a)   Suggest what type of pencil would have been used for the initial freehand sketches of the sign.

....

(1 mark)

b)   Suggest an appropriate medium to use for the **lettering** on the presentation drawing.

....

(1 mark)

c)   Suggest an appropriate medium for the **background** of the presentation drawing, and give an advantage of using that medium.

Make sure you pick a medium you can give an advantage for.

Medium: ....

Advantage: ....

(2 marks)

Adhesives

1   Suggest **one** material that each type of adhesive in **Table 1** could be used on.

Table 1

Adhesive	Suitable material
	....
	....
	....

(3 marks)

2   A designer is making a model of a DVD box using card.

a)   The designer does not want to use glue. Suggest another way that the designer could stick the net together so that the adhesive and tabs cannot be seen.

....
(1 mark)

b)   Suggest a method of protecting the model after it is has been assembled.

....
(1 mark)

3   Suggest **one** suitable adhesive for each of the following joins.

a)   Balsa wood to balsa wood ....
(1 mark)

b)   A poster to a wall ....
(1 mark)

c)   Paper to paper ....
(1 mark)

d)   Paper to a drawing board ....
(1 mark)

e)   Plastic to ceramic ....
(1 mark)

f)   Paper to wood ....
(1 mark)

g)   Acrylic to acrylic ....
(1 mark)

Tools — 1

1   **Figure 1** shows a pop-up greetings card made of thin card. A batch of 20 cards will be made.

Figure 1

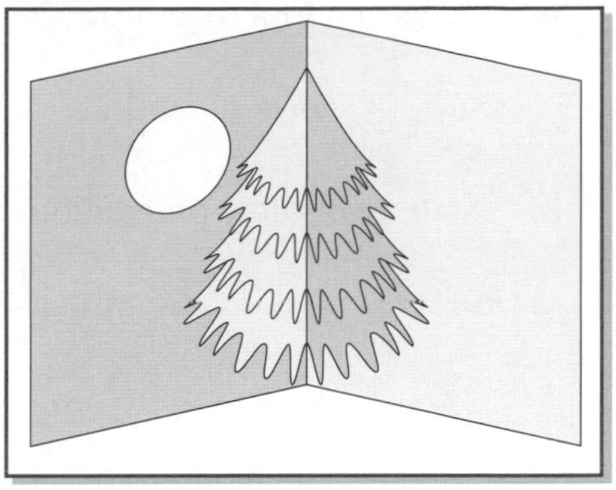

a) The card has a circular hole in the front.
    Suggest a suitable tool for cutting out the circle.

    ....
                                                                    (1 mark)

b) i) The main part of the card is a rectangle folded in half.
        Suggest a suitable tool for cutting out the rectangle.

        ....
                                                                    (1 mark)

    ii) Give **two** advantages of using that tool.

        ....

        ....
                                                                    (2 marks)

c) i) A surgical scalpel will be used to cut out the pop-up tree.
        Give **one** advantage of using a scalpel.

        ....
                                                                    (1 mark)

    ii) Give the safety precautions that are needed when using a scalpel.

        ....

        ....
                                                                    (2 marks)

2   Complete the details for each piece of equipment below.

a)   Name of equipment: ....

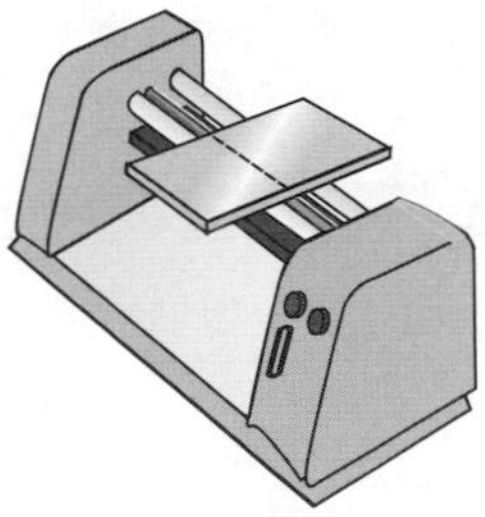

                    Use: ....

                    ....
                                                                    (2 marks)

b)   Name of equipment: ....

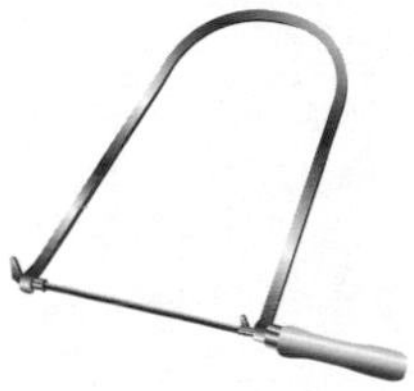

                    Use: ....

                    ....
                                                                    (2 marks)

Section 2 — Materials and Components

Tools — 2

3   STYROFOAM™ can crumble if cut with a craft knife.

a)   Suggest a tool that allows STYROFOAM™ to be cut easily.

....

(1 mark)

b)   State **two** safety precautions that should be taken when cutting STYROFOAM™.

....

....

(2 marks)

4   **Figure 2** shows a design for a model of a stage set.

Describe with sketches and notes how this model would be constructed. Marks will be awarded for describing the tools and equipment.

Figure 2

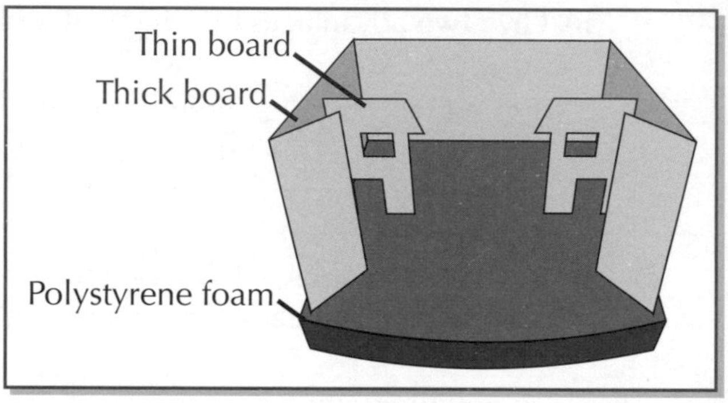

Thin board
Thick board
Polystyrene foam

Break the answer down into step-by-step instructions — you're less likely to forget something then.

(6 marks)

Section 2 — Materials and Components

Fixings and Bindings

1   **Table 1** shows different types of fixings. State whether each fixing is
     permanent or temporary, and suggest **one** purpose it might be used for.

Table 1

Fixing	Permanent or temporary	Purpose
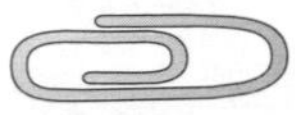	....	....
	....	....
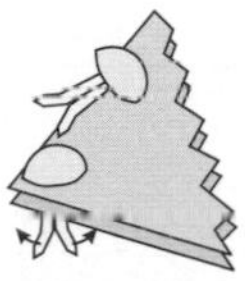	....	....
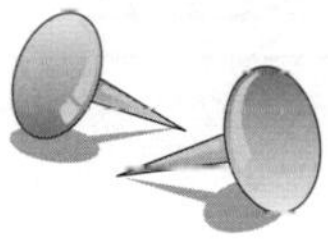	....	....

(8 marks)

2   **Figure 1** shows a 12-page A4 brochure which
     is to be made by binding sheets of paper.

Figure 1

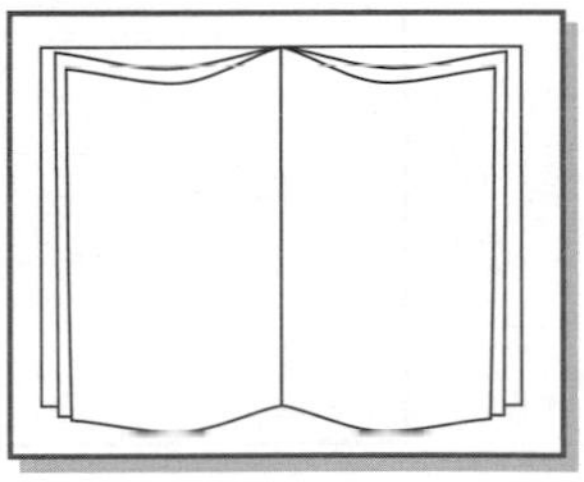

a)   Name a method of binding that could be used for the brochure.

     ....
                                                                          (1 mark)

b)   Describe how the brochure would be bound using this method.

     ....

     ....

     ....
                                                                          (3 marks)

c)   Give **two** advantages of this type of binding.

     ....

     ....
                                                                          (2 marks)

Section 2 — Materials and Components

Sketching — 1

1 A local vet wants a logo that includes the name 'Creature Aid' and appropriate images.

Sketch and annotate **two** different design ideas for the logo.

Annotate means to add notes.

(6 marks)

2 A client needs a logo for a new fruit cereal bar for children.
It must include appropriate images and the name 'Fruit Fun'.

a) Sketch and annotate **three** design ideas in the space below.

(9 marks)

b) Develop **one** of your ideas to create a final logo.

(3 marks)

Sketching — 2

3 A food company wants to create new packaging for their sandwiches.

a) Use the **crating** technique to draw and annotate **two** ideas for the packaging.

You could include notes on materials and construction details.

(6 marks)

b) i) Using the grid below, develop **one** of your ideas into a final design.
Add notes to show materials and construction details.

(4 marks)

ii) Name the type of grid shown above.

....

(1 mark)

Shading and Texture — 1

1   Use pencil to render this drawing of a camera made from matt plastic.
    Bear in mind the light source shown.

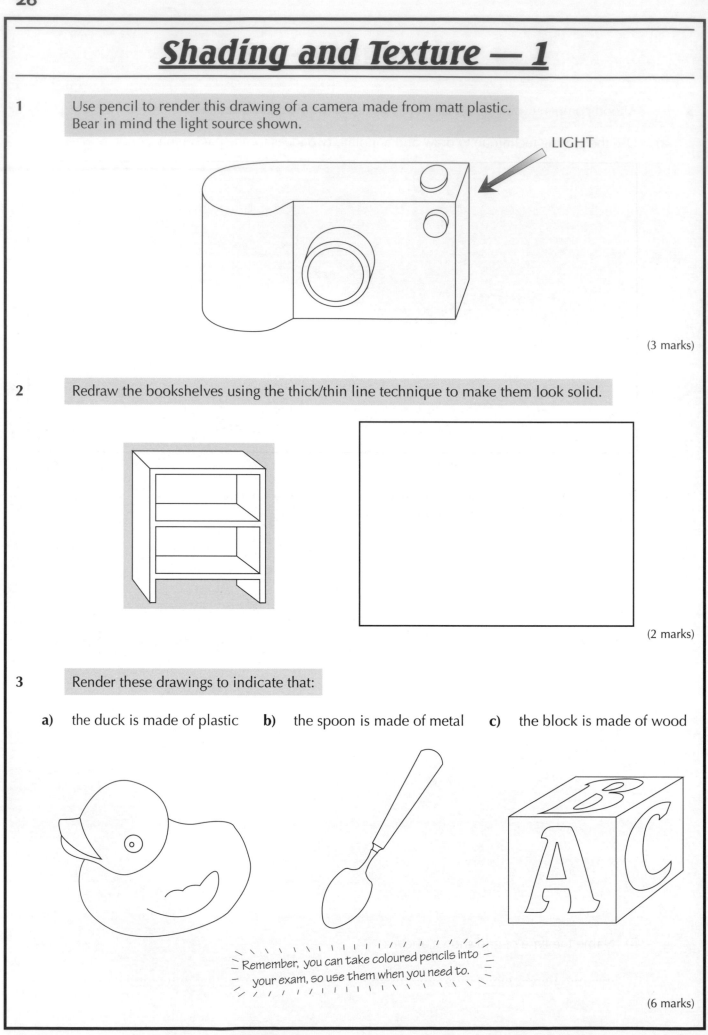

LIGHT

(3 marks)

2   Redraw the bookshelves using the thick/thin line technique to make them look solid.

(2 marks)

3   Render these drawings to indicate that:

a) the duck is made of plastic   b) the spoon is made of metal   c) the block is made of wood

Remember, you can take coloured pencils into
your exam, so use them when you need to.

(6 marks)

Shading and Texture — 2

4 Figure 1 shows the design for a new mobile phone. The screen will be shiny plastic, the phone will be smooth, coloured plastic and the buttons will be silver metal.

Render the drawing to suggest these materials and add thick/thin lines to make the object look more solid. Make sure you take into account the light source shining from the left.

Figure 1

(5 marks)

5 A computer software company, 'Softfruit Inc.', have a new logo.

a) Render the logo to show how it would look **embossed**.

(2 marks)

Foil application gives a shiny look.

b) Render the logo to show how it would look with a **foil finish**.

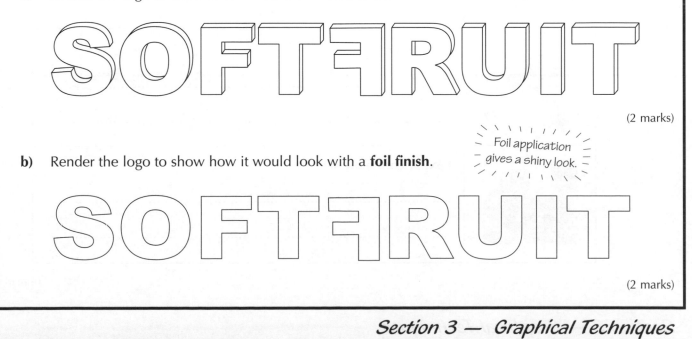

(2 marks)

Section 3 — Graphical Techniques

Colour and Mood

1   Explain what is meant by the following terms:

a)   hue ....

                                                                               (1 mark)

b)   tone ....

                                                                               (1 mark)

2   This question is about colour.

a)   Briefly explain what complementary colours are.

     ....

     ....

                                                                              (2 marks)

b)   **i)**   State the colour that is complementary to purple.

         ....

                                                                                    (1 mark)

     ii)   State whether this colour is a primary or a secondary colour.

         ....

                                                                                     (1 mark)

3   Suggest colours for the products below. Explain your answers.
       One example has been given.

PEDESTRIANS PROHIBITED	**Road sign** Red can represent danger so could be used for a sign that gives a warning.
	Hair dryer ....
	Luxury chocolate box ....

                                                                                               (4 marks)

Colour Fusion and Separation

1 Printers use processing colours and special spot colours.

a) Name the four processing colours used in printing.

1. ....

2. ....

3. ....

4. ....

(4 marks)

Talk about collar fusion...

b) **i)** Explain why some printers use spot colours.

....

....

(1 mark)

ii) Give an example of where a spot colour may be used.

....

(1 mark)

2 Many graphic products use colour fusion.

a) Explain the term colour fusion.

....

....

(2 marks)

b) Give an example of a product where colour fusion is used.

....

(1 mark)

3 Explain how a digital scanner separates an image into different colours for printing.

....

....

....

....

(4 marks)

Make sure you give four clear points to get all four marks.

Section 3 — Graphical Techniques

Lettering and Presentation — 1

1   Designers often show their client a 3D presentation drawing and a working drawing of the design idea.

a)   Describe what a working drawing shows a client.

....

....

(1 mark)

b)   Describe what a 3D presentation drawing shows.

....

....

(1 mark)

2   CAD can be used to manipulate and present a design.

a)   Give **three** ways that CAD can be used to manipulate drawings.

1.   ....

2.   ....

3.   ....

(3 marks)

b)   State **two** advantages of using CAD to present a design.

1.   ....

2.   ....

(2 marks)

3   This question is about photo manipulation.

Photo manipulation just means changing a photo in some way.

a)   Give **two** examples of photo manipulation software.

1.   ....

2.   ....

(2 marks)

b)   Describe **three** ways that photographs can be changed using photo manipulation software.

1.   ....

2.   ....

3.   ....

(3 marks)

Lettering and Presentation — 2

4 State whether each lettering styles is serif, sans serif or script.

a) *Sausage* ....

b) jellyfish ....

c) alien slime ....

(3 marks)

5 The table below gives four products which have lettering in their design. Design a suitable font for each one. One example has been given.

Just pick a word or two that is relevant to the product.

Product	Font Style
Poster advertising a ballet	*New Ballet*
Business card for a limousine driver	
Birthday card for a young child	
Flyer for a fashionable new nightclub	

(6 marks)

6 Products such as menus are often encapsulated.

a) Give **two** reasons why this is done.

....

....

(2 marks)

b) Briefly describe the encapsulation process.

....

....

....

....

(3 marks)

Pictorial Drawings — 1

1   Perspective drawing is one type of three-dimensional drawing.

Give one advantage of drawing in perspective.

....

(1 mark)

2   **Figure 1** shows a design for a tissue box.

Make a one-point perspective drawing of the tissue box.

Figure 1

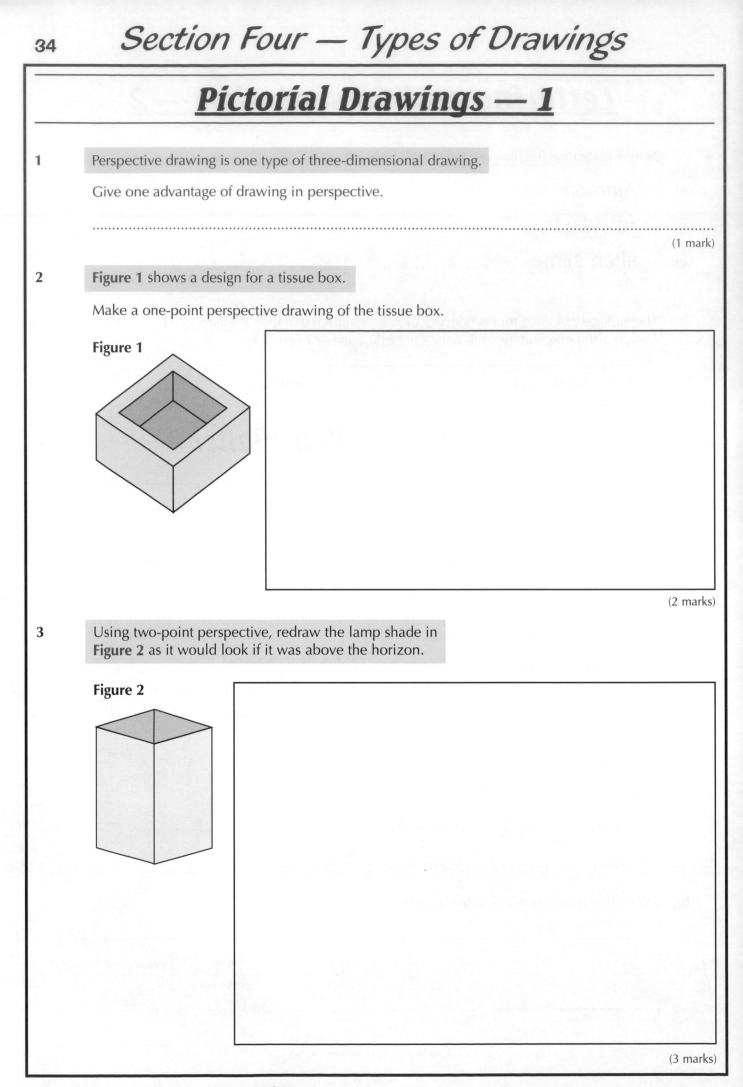

(2 marks)

3   Using two-point perspective, redraw the lamp shade in **Figure 2** as it would look if it was above the horizon.

Figure 2

(3 marks)

Pictorial Drawings — 2

4 Isometric drawing is one way to present designs.

a) Give **two** reasons why a designer might use isometric drawings to present a design idea.

....

....

(2 marks)

b) Use the isometric grid below to produce a **wireframe** drawing of a box 30 mm wide, 40 mm deep and 20 mm high.

10 mm

(4 marks)

5 Draw a freehand isometric sketch of a design for packaging for an Easter egg. The box must be taller than it is wide, and have a window in the front.

(3 marks)

<u>*Working Drawings — 1*</u>

1   Figure 1 shows a design for a toaster.

a)   Complete **Figure 1** by naming the two other **views** that are shown in a third angle orthographic projection.

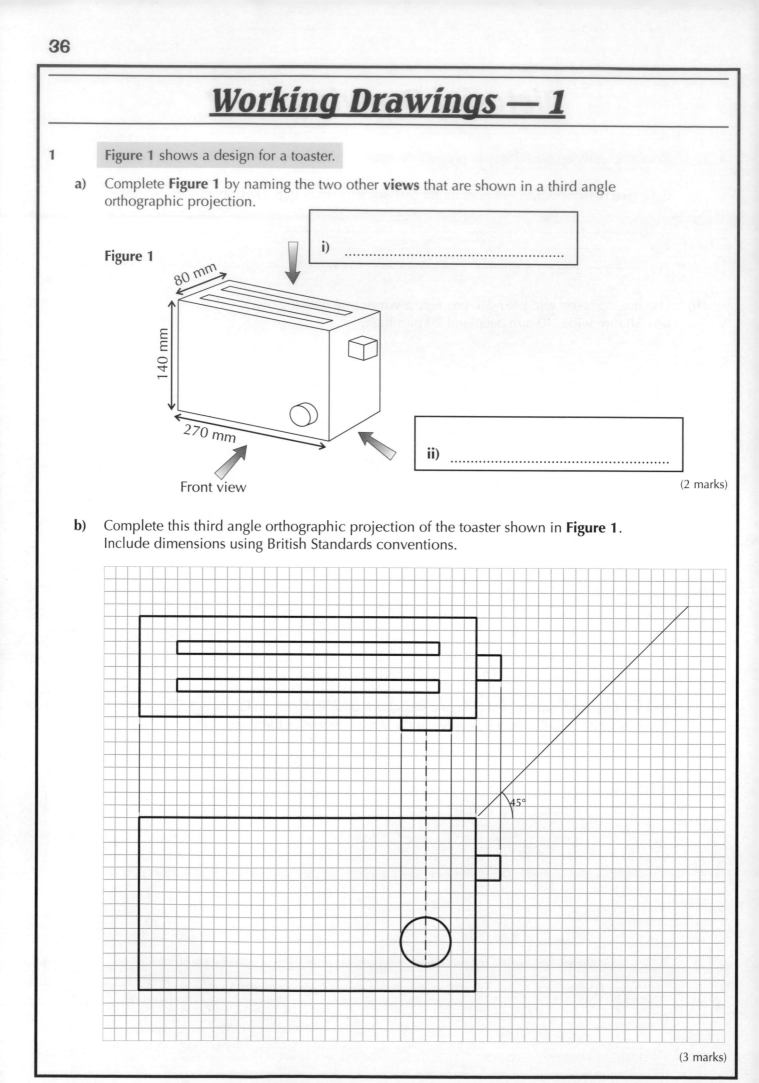

i) ....

ii) ....

(2 marks)

b)   Complete this third angle orthographic projection of the toaster shown in **Figure 1**. Include dimensions using British Standards conventions.

(3 marks)

Working Drawings — 2

2 The bookcase in **Figure 2** needs to be assembled at home by the consumer.
Instructions are needed to help the consumer assemble it.

a) Name **one** style of drawing that would be suitable for the instructions.
Explain why this style of drawing is suitable.

....

....

(2 marks)

b) Draw assembly instructions for the bookcase using this style of drawing.

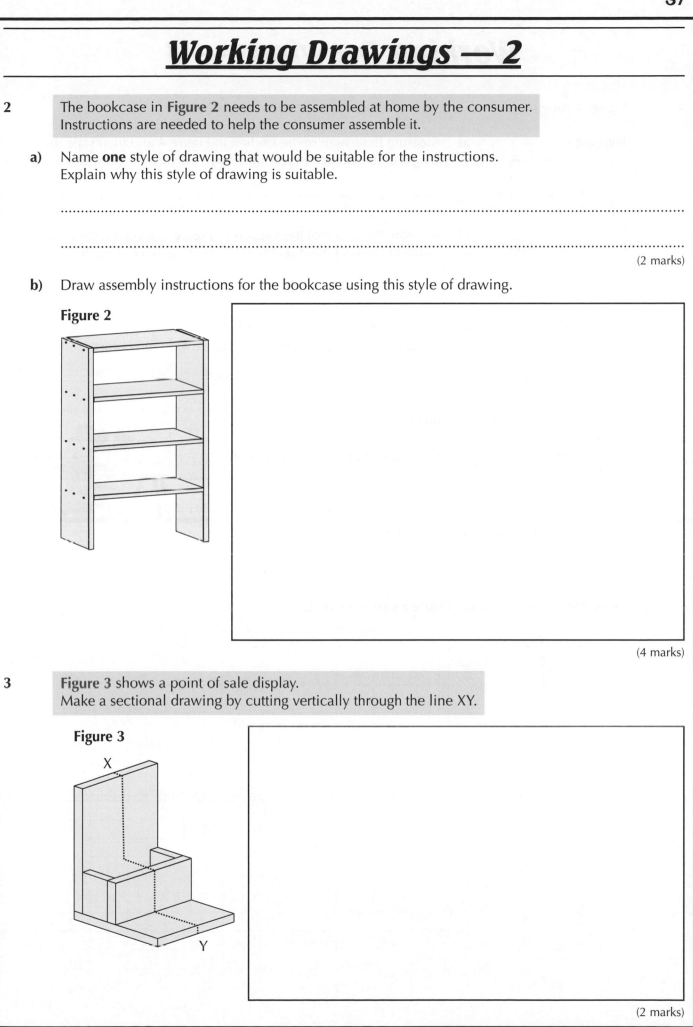

Figure 2

(4 marks)

3 **Figure 3** shows a point of sale display.
Make a sectional drawing by cutting vertically through the line XY.

Figure 3

X

Y

(2 marks)

Section 4 — Types of Drawings

Working Drawings — 3

4   Figure 4 shows a plan of a kitchen which is drawn at 1:100 scale.

Figure 4

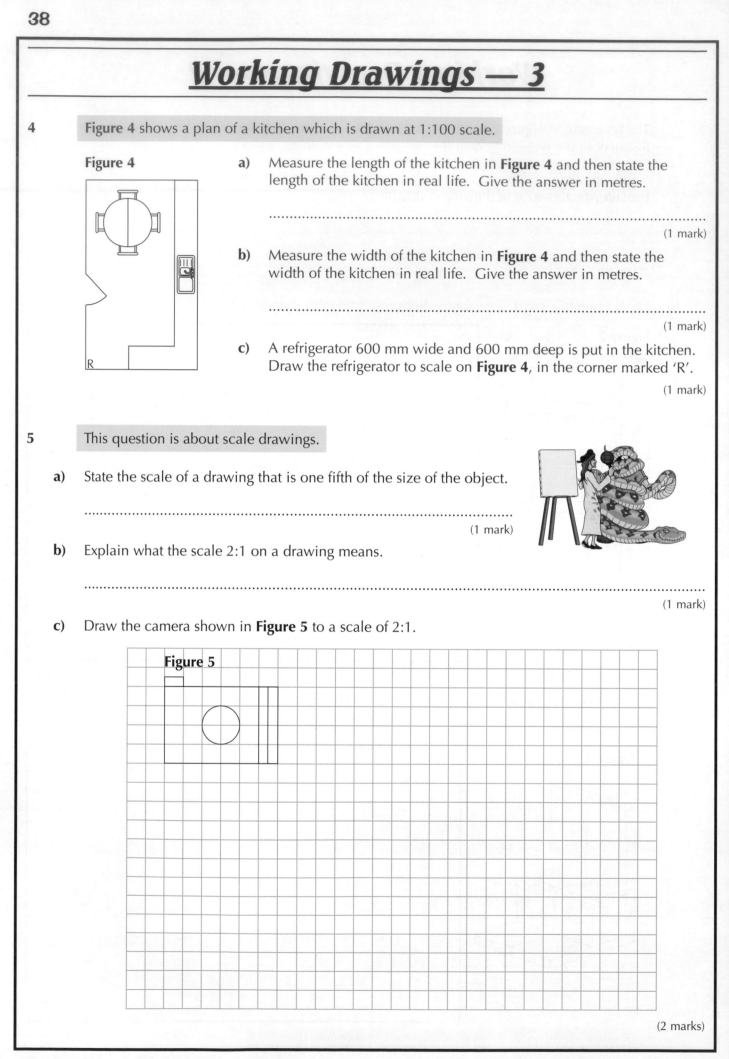

a)   Measure the length of the kitchen in **Figure 4** and then state the length of the kitchen in real life. Give the answer in metres.

....

(1 mark)

b)   Measure the width of the kitchen in **Figure 4** and then state the width of the kitchen in real life. Give the answer in metres.

....

(1 mark)

c)   A refrigerator 600 mm wide and 600 mm deep is put in the kitchen. Draw the refrigerator to scale on **Figure 4**, in the corner marked 'R'.

(1 mark)

5   This question is about scale drawings.

a)   State the scale of a drawing that is one fifth of the size of the object.

....

(1 mark)

b)   Explain what the scale 2:1 on a drawing means.

....

(1 mark)

c)   Draw the camera shown in **Figure 5** to a scale of 2:1.

Figure 5

(2 marks)

Working Drawings — 4

6   **Figure 6** shows the bus routes around a city.

Figure 6

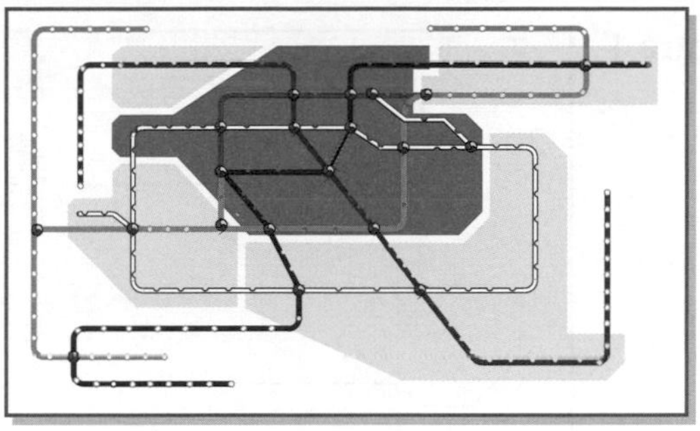

a)   Name this type of drawing.

....
(1 mark)

b)   i)   Give **one** advantage of this style of drawing.

....
(1 mark)

ii)   Give **one** disadvantage of this style of drawing.

....
(1 mark)

c)   **Figure 7** shows the main roads that link a number of UK cities.
Draw a map of these routes in the same style as **Figure 6**.

Figure 7

(2 marks)

d)   Evaluate how useful this map would be for drivers.

....

....

....
(2 marks)

<u>Nets and Packaging — 1</u>

1   **Figure 1** shows a surface development of a gift box.

'Surface development' means the same as 'net'.

Figure 1

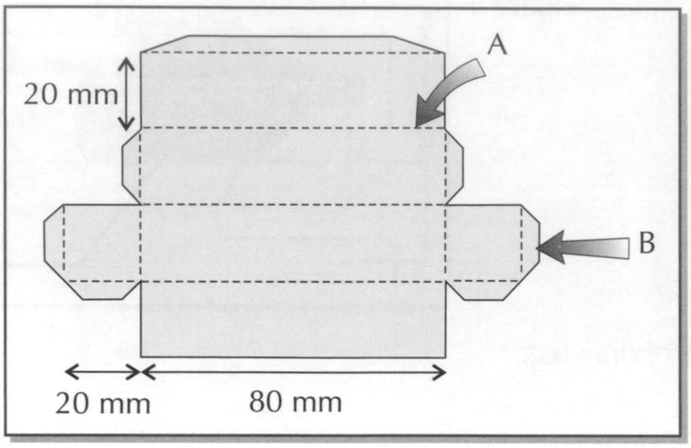

20 mm

A

B

20 mm   80 mm

a)   State what the line labelled **A** means.

....

(1 mark)

b)   State what the part labelled **B** is used for.

....

....

(1 mark)

c)   Do a freehand isometric drawing of the assembled gift box.

10 mm

(3 marks)

Nets and Packaging — 2

2   Draw an accurate surface development for the 3D shape shown in **Figure 2**.

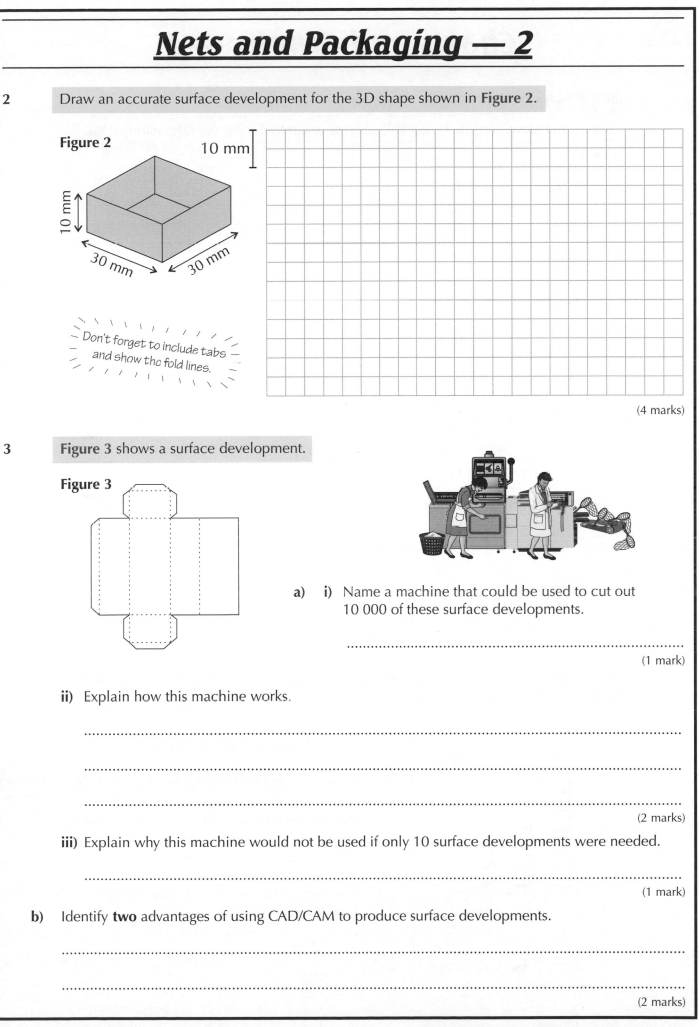

Figure 2

10 mm

10 mm

30 mm   30 mm

Don't forget to include tabs and show the fold lines.

(4 marks)

3   **Figure 3** shows a surface development.

Figure 3

a)   i) Name a machine that could be used to cut out 10 000 of these surface developments.

....

(1 mark)

ii) Explain how this machine works.

....

....

....

(2 marks)

iii) Explain why this machine would not be used if only 10 surface developments were needed.

....

(1 mark)

b) Identify **two** advantages of using CAD/CAM to produce surface developments.

....

....

(2 marks)

Section 4 — Types of Drawings

Charts and Graphs — 1

1   Table 1 shows the sales of a new magazine.

   a)   On the grid below, construct a suitable chart or graph to display the sales information.

Table 1

Month	Sales
January	2500
February	3000
March	4000
April	2000
May	1500
June	1000

(5 marks)

   b)   **i)**   Name the type of chart or graph you have drawn.

....

(1 mark)

         ii)   Explain why you chose this type of chart or graph.

....

....

(1 mark)

2   Birdwatchers recorded the number of birds at a local pond on the first day of each month. **Figure 1** shows their results for January, April and July.

Figure 1

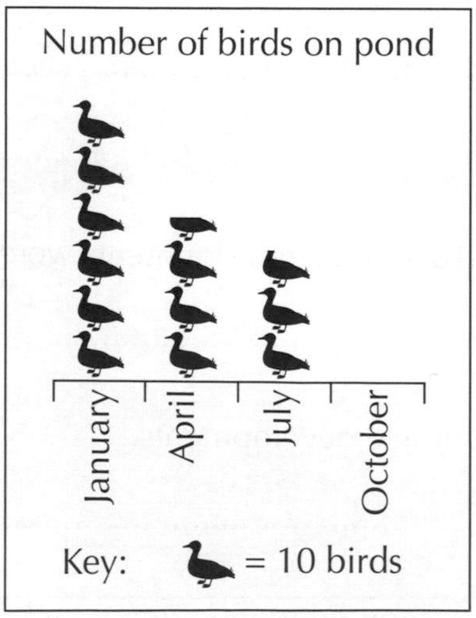

   a)   Give the name of this type of graph.

....

(1 mark)

   b)   State the number of birds seen on 1st January.

....

(1 mark)

   c)   Complete the graph to show that 40 birds were seen on 1st October.

(1 mark)

Section 4 — Types of Drawings

Charts and Graphs — 2

3   Draw a pie chart to show the following market research survey results.

Most effective poster colour:
Red 50%, Blue 25%, Green 15%, Purple 10%.

Remember to label the pie chart.

(4 marks)

4   This question is about sequential illustrations.

a)   Complete the sequential illustration to show the first three steps of making a paper aeroplane.

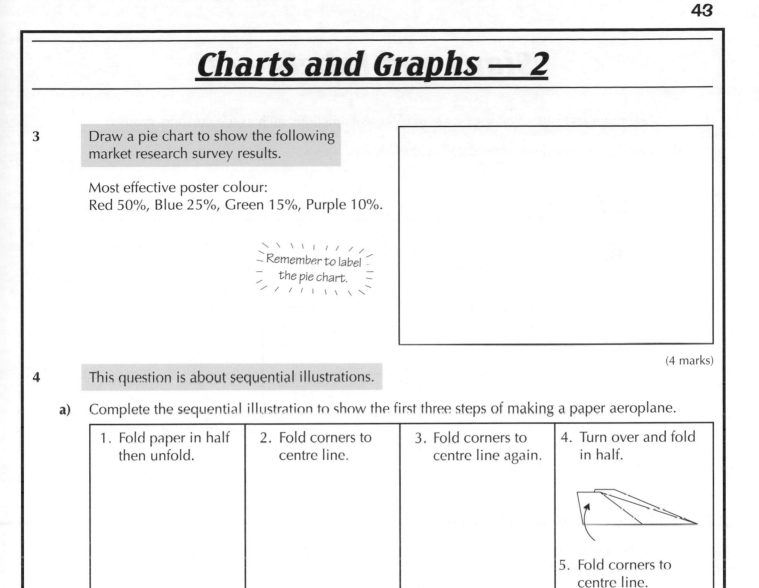

1. Fold paper in half then unfold.	2. Fold corners to centre line.	3. Fold corners to centre line again.	4. Turn over and fold in half.
			5. Fold corners to centre line.

(3 marks)

b)   Draw a flow chart to show the same process. Include a quality control check and a feedback loop.

(4 marks)

Signs and Labels — 1

1   Computer software often uses **icons** to represent functions such as 'delete' and 'paste'.

a)   Identify the functions represented by these icons.

i)   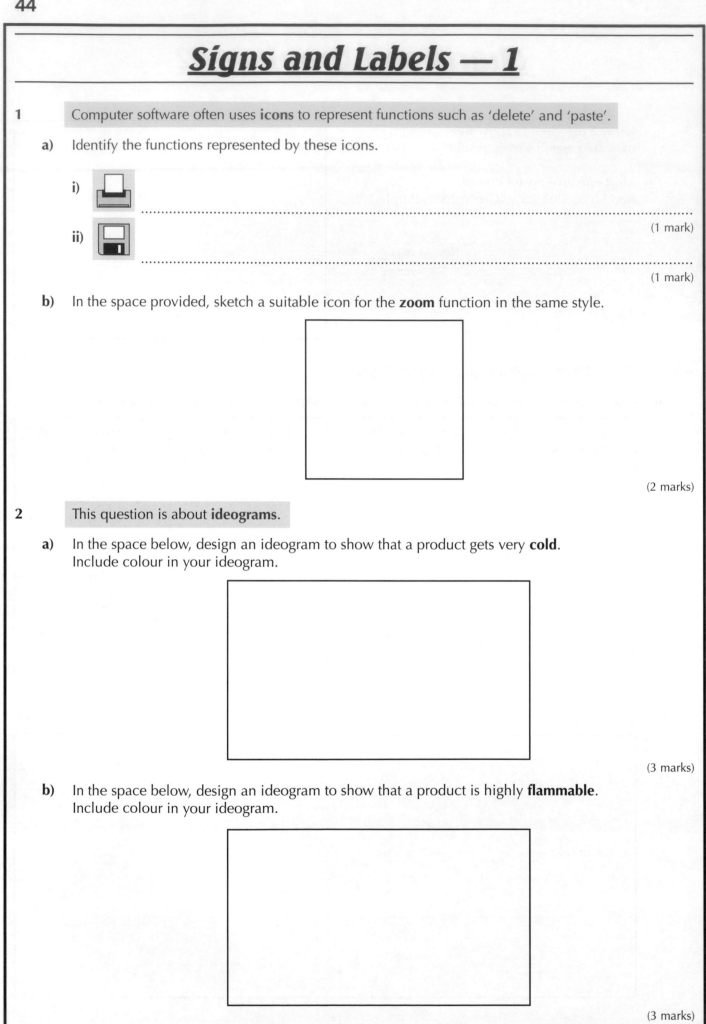 ....

(1 mark)

ii)   ....

(1 mark)

b)   In the space provided, sketch a suitable icon for the **zoom** function in the same style.

(2 marks)

2   This question is about **ideograms**.

a)   In the space below, design an ideogram to show that a product gets very **cold**.
Include colour in your ideogram.

(3 marks)

b)   In the space below, design an ideogram to show that a product is highly **flammable**.
Include colour in your ideogram.

(3 marks)

Section 4 — Types of Drawings

Signs and Labels — 2

3   Product packaging often includes labels.

a)   Give **two** reasons why a product might need to be labelled.

....

....

(2 marks)

b)   Give the meaning of each of the following symbols:

i)   200ml ℮

....

(1 mark)

ii)

....

(1 mark)

iii)

18 M

....

(1 mark)

4   **Figure 1** shows the packaging for a quiche.

Figure 1

Broccoli and Stilton Quiche

V

a)   Explain what the 'V' symbol on the packaging means.

....

(1 mark)

b)   The quiche may contain traces of nuts. Draw a label suitable for the packaging to indicate this. Include a symbol.

(1 mark)

c)   Another symbol on the quiche packaging is shown in **Figure 2**. State the **name** of the symbol and give **one use** for it.

Figure 2

5 000143 057629

....

....

(2 marks)

Section 4 — Types of Drawings

Branding and Social Responsibility

1   Companies use logos to enhance their corporate identity.

    a) **i)** Explain what is meant by the term 'corporate identity'.

....

....

(2 marks)

        ii) Suggest **two** places where a company could display its logo.

1. ....

2. ....

(2 marks)

    b) Sketch and annotate **one** suitable logo for Pete's Pizzas.
The logo should use colour, appeal to families and advertise the product.

(4 marks)

2   Suggest **two** ways a company could create the image of being morally responsible.

....

....

(2 marks)

3   Sometimes companies need to change the name or design of a product before selling it abroad.

    a) Suggest why designers need to research the name of a product before selling it in other countries.

....

(1 mark)

    b) Give **one** other example of something designers need to take into account for international sales.

....

(1 mark)

<u>Packaging and Sustainability — 1</u>

1 Some types of packaging are designed to help **protect** either the consumers or the product.

a) **i)** Explain what is meant by a 'tamper-evident seal'.

....
(1 mark)

ii) Suggest **one** product that might have a tamper-evident seal.

....
(1 mark)

b) Products need to be protected during transportation.
Suggest how a product could be packaged for transport.

....
(1 mark)

c) Name and describe **three** other functions of packaging.

1. ....

....

2. ....

....

3. ....

....
(6 marks)

2 Discuss the environmental impact of packaging.

....

....

....

....
(4 marks)

3 Suggest **three** reasons why a customer might choose not to buy a product with too much packaging.

....

....

....
(3 marks)

Packaging and Sustainability — 2

4   Table 1 lists the 6 Rs.

a)   Fill in the table to explain how designers can reduce the environmental impact of products.

For this question, make sure you talk about the designers, not the consumers.

Table 1

R	Explanation
Reduce	
Recycle	
Repair	
Re-use	
Refuse	
Re-think	

(6 marks)

b)   Give **one** problem of reusing products.

....

....

(1 mark)

The 6Rs do have some problems, so make sure you know these too.

c)   Give **one** problem of recycling materials.

....

....

(1 mark)

Section 5 — Society and the Environment

Legal Issues and Standards — 1

1   This question is about laws and regulations.

a)   Many products make claims about their function.
Name the set of regulations which ensure that these claims are true.

....

(1 mark)

b)   Explain the purpose of the General Product Safety Regulations.

....

(1 mark)

c)   **i)**   Give a type of product that is covered by the Fire Safety Regulations

....

(1 mark)

     ii)   Describe the conditions a product must satisfy to meet these regulations

....

....

(2 marks)

2   Designers need to stop competitors from stealing their designs and ideas.

a)   **i)**   Briefly describe what a patent is.

....

....

....

(3 marks)

     ii)   Give **one** example of a design that has been protected by a patent.

....

(1 mark)

b)   **i)**   Name the law that would protect a new comic book.

....

(1 mark)

     ii)   Suggest how the logo on the comic book would be protected.

....

(1 mark)

Legal Issues and Standards — 2

3   Some laws are put in place to protect workers.

Write out what COSHH stands for and explain what these regulations are for.

....

....

(2 marks)

4   **Figures 1** and **2** show two different standards symbols.

Figure 1   **Figure 2**

a)   **i)**   Give the name of the symbol in **Figure 1**.

....

(1 mark)

ii)   Explain the meaning of the symbol in **Figure 1**.

....

(1 mark)

b)   **i)**   Describe what the symbol in **Figure 2** shows.

....

(1 mark)

ii)   Suggest a product where it might be found.

....

(1 mark)

c)   Draw the symbol that would be awarded to a product that had fulfilled standards tested by the British Standards Institution.

(2 marks)

d)   Give **two** reasons why a consumer is more likely to buy a product that is labelled to show it meets certain standards.

....

....

(2 marks)

Section 5 — Society and the Environment

Health and Safety — 1

1   The Health and Safety at Work Act ensures that employers provide a safe working environment.

Give **two** ways an employer could work towards creating a safe working environment

1. ....

2. ....

(2 marks)

2   Name **two** pieces of clothing that can protect people in a workshop.

1. ....

2. ....

(2 marks)

3   **Table 1** lists three tools. Describe the safety precautions workers must observe when using each tool.

Table 1

Tool	Safety Precautions
Craft knife	....
Saw	....
Hot wire cutter	....

(3 marks)

4   Suggest appropriate safety precautions for these situations.

a)   Handling pieces of rough sawn wood that will be used to make a product.

....

(1 mark)

b)   Storing heavy boxes.

....

(1 mark)

Health and Safety — 2

5   Employers must carry out a risk assessment for any new projects.

Explain what is meant by a 'risk assessment'.

....

....

(2 marks)

6   **Table 2** shows some of the stages of designing and making a gift box.
Complete the risk assessment for this process.

Table 2

Process	Hazard	How to minimise the risk
Design graphics using CAD	....	....
Cut net from card	....	....
Apply graphics using spray adhesive	....	....
Assemble using hot glue gun	....	....

(12 marks)

For each process you get one mark for giving the hazard and two marks for explaining how to minimise the risk.

CAD/CAM — 1

1 Computer Aided Design (CAD) programs use **icons** to represent drawing tools.

a) Four icons are shown in the table below. Fill in the details for each icon. One example is given.

Icon	Description	Use
☐	Box tool	To draw squares and rectangles on the design
▲	....	....
◈	....	....
A	....	....

(6 marks)

b) **i)** Give **one** advantage of using CAD for a designer.

....
(1 mark)

ii) Give **one** advantage of CAD for the client who commissions a design.

....
(1 mark)

2 **CAD/CAM** is used in many industrial production systems.

a) Explain what is meant by CAD/CAM.

....
(1 mark)

b) Explain **one** advantage and **one** disadvantage of using CAM.

i) Advantage: ....

....
(2 marks)

ii) Disadvantage: ....

....
(2 marks)

CAD/CAM — 2

3 **Figure 1** shows a design for a sign. The letters are raised above the background.

Figure 1

a) Use notes and sketches to show how you would make a batch of eight of these signs using CAD/CAM. Name the tools, equipment and software you would use at each stage.

First stage: Computer Aided Design (CAD)

(4 marks)

Second stage: Computer Aided Manufacture (CAM)

(4 marks)

b) CAM machines are computer numerically controlled (CNC).
Explain what is meant by the term 'computer numerically controlled'.

....

....

....

(3 marks)

ICT — 1

1   **Computers** are made up of hardware and software.

a)   Describe the difference between hardware and software.

....

....

(2 marks)

b)   Give an example of:

i)   hardware: ....

(1 mark)

ii) software: ....

(1 mark)

2   ICT equipment includes **input** devices and **output** devices.

a)   Explain what is meant by the term 'input device'.

....

(1 mark)

b)   Three ICT devices are shown below.
Name each item, state whether it is an input or output device and describe its use.

i)

Name ....

Type of device ....

Use ....

....

(3 marks)

ii)

Name ....

Type of device ....

Use ....

....

(3 marks)

iii)

Name ....

Type of device ....

Use ....

....

(3 marks)

ICT — 2

3 A range of **software programs** exist to do different tasks. Suggest the type of program that could be used to:

a) work out production costs and time management,

....
(1 mark)

b) manipulate photographs.

....
(1 mark)

You don't need to name a specific program, just a type of software.

4 ICT means industries can transfer data **electronically**.

a) Suggest a simple way to electronically transfer written information.

....
(1 mark)

b) Explain **one** benefit of being able to transfer data electronically.

....

....
(2 marks)

c) Give **two other** benefits of using ICT in industry.

1. ....

2. ....
(2 marks)

d) Explain **two** problems associated with using ICT in industry.

1. ....

....

2. ....

....
(4 marks)

Systems and Quality Control — 1

1   Flow charts can be used to show manufacturing systems.

a)   Study the flow chart below, which shows a system for copying hand-drawn leaflets.
Draw a feedback loop on the flow chart to show that if the information isn't clear,
the settings on the photocopier should be checked and the photocopying done again.

```
Start → Photocopy    → Is the      Yes → Trim paper → Fold leaflet → Stop
         the leaflet     information       to size       in half
                         clear?
```

(3 marks)

b)   Systems include inputs, processes and outputs.
Name **two** processes shown in the flow chart above, and give the output of the whole system.

Process 1: ....

Process 2: ....

Output: ....

(3 marks)

2   A sign maker was commissioned to make 20 signs with lettering and a logo.

The logo was stencilled onto squares of MDF, and then stick-on letters were applied.
The signs were checked to make sure the letters were straight.
Any letters that weren't straight were re-applied. Finally the signs were attached to poles.

a)   Name an input and the output of this manufacturing system.

Input: ....

Output: ....

(2 marks)

b)   Draw a flow chart to show the process. Include a feedback loop.

```
Think carefully about where the
feedback loop should go back to.
```

(5 marks)

Systems and Quality Control — 2

3   Manufacturers include **quality control checks** in their manufacturing processes.

a)   Give **three** reasons why they do this.

1. ....

2. ....

3. ....

(3 marks)

b)   Suggest **two** ways that a greetings card could be checked for quality.

1. ....

2. ....

(2 marks)

c)   Quality control checks are part of the system of quality assurance.
Suggest another process that is important for quality assurance.

....

(1 mark)

4   A design for a ketchup label is shown below.

40 mm

50 mm

Bob's Organic
Tomato Ketchup

100% natural ingredients

simple logo

logo centred
on label

pale red
background

water-soluble
glue to help
recycling

clear, sharp
printed picture

show a tomato cut open
to suggest freshness

a)   Give **two** quality control checks that could be
made on the label.

1. ....

....

....

2. ....

....

....

(2 marks)

b)   The label is going to be stuck onto bottles, 25 mm ± 2 mm from the base.

(i) State the greatest acceptable distance between the bottom of the bottle and the label.

....

(1 mark)

(ii) Suggest **one** other thing about the label that should be checked after it has been stuck on.

....

(1 mark)

Scale of Production — 1

1 This question is about **batch production**.

a) Explain what is meant by 'batch production'.

....

....
(2 marks)

b) Suggest a graphics product that could be made by batch production.

....
(1 mark)

c) Suggest why a firm using batch production needs a flexible workforce and adjustable machinery.

....

....
(1 mark)

d) Explain why batch production is not as efficient as mass production.

....

....
(1 mark)

2 Many products are manufactured using **continuous production**.

a) Explain what is meant by the term 'continuous production'.

....

....
(2 marks)

b) Give **two** advantages of making things by continuous production.

....

....
(2 marks)

c) **Figure 1** shows a range of magazines and newspapers. Suggest why continuous production is not suitable for making products such as these.

Figure 1

....

....
(1 mark)

Scale of Production — 2

3   Some products are **mass produced**.

a)   Explain what sorts of products are suitable for mass production. Give an example.

....

....

(2 marks)

b)   Suggest why mass production might be expensive to set up.

....

(1 mark)

c)   Suggest why it might be easy to recruit mass production workers.

....

(1 mark)

4   Manufacturers sometimes choose to use a **just-in-time system**.

a)   Briefly describe what a just-in-time system is.

....

....

....

(2 marks)

Justin Time...

b)   Give **one** advantage and **one** disadvantage of just-in-time systems.

   i)   Advantage: ....

(1 mark)

   ii) Disadvantage: ....

(1 mark)

5   A **one-off prototype** for a cereal box is produced by printing the design onto card, cutting out the net, and then folding up the box.

a)   Suggest how the production method would change when the box was mass produced.

....

....

(2 marks)

b)   Explain why production methods are often simplified for mass production.

....

....

(1 mark)

Packaging and Mechanisms — 1

1   Some packaging is formed by **blow moulding**.

a)   Briefly describe how packaging is formed using blow moulding.

....

....

....

(3 marks)

b)   Suggest **one** product that could be made using blow moulding.

....

(1 mark)

2   12 000 new cameras are to be made. They will be packaged in **rigid polystyrene trays** inside **cardboard sleeves**.

a)   **i)**   Suggest a process that could be used to form the polystyrene trays.

....

(1 mark)

     ii)   Briefly describe this process.

....

....

....

(3 marks)

b)   **i)**   Suggest an efficient method of cutting out 12 000 nets for the sleeves.

....

(1 mark)

     ii)   Briefly describe this method.

....

....

....

(3 marks)

     iii)   Give **one** advantage of using this method to cut out the nets and explain your answer.

....

....

(2 marks)

Packaging and Mechanisms — 2

3 Some greetings cards have features such as **moving parts** and **integrated circuits**.

a) Suggest why pop-ups are sometimes used in children's birthday cards.

....

....

(1 mark)

b) i) Name the **four** different types of motion that moving parts in a card could have.

1. ....

2. ....

3. ....

4. ....

(4 marks)

ii) Explain the difference between floating pivots and fixed pivots.

....

....

(2 marks)

c) Suggest **one** use for an integrated circuit in a greetings card.

....

(1 mark)

d) Use sketches and notes to design a birthday card with moving parts.

Remember to show how
the moving parts will work.

(4 marks)

Printing — Commercial Methods — 1

1   One commercial printing method is **lithography**.

a)   Describe the process of printing using lithography.

....

....

....

....

....

(4 marks)

b)   Give **two** examples of products that are commonly printed using lithography.

1.   ....

2.   ....

(2 marks)

c)   Give **two** advantages of lithography.

1.   ....

2.   ....

(2 marks)

2   This question is about printing using **flexography**.

a)   State the materials that the printing plates used in flexography are made from.

....

(1 mark)

b)   Name **two** products that can be printed using flexography.

1.   ....

2.   ....

(2 marks)

c)   Give **two** reasons why flexography might be used instead of lithography.

....

....

(2 marks)

d)   Suggest a print run size for which it would be appropriate to use flexography.

....

(1 mark)

Bernard wondered what had happened to good old-fashioned ink and parchment.

Printing — Commercial Methods — 2

3   Some products are printed by the process of **gravure**.

a)   Briefly describe this process.

....

....

....

(3 marks)

b) **i)** Give **one** advantage of gravure.

....

(1 mark)

ii) Give **one** disadvantage of gravure.

....

(1 mark)

c)   Name **two** products that can be printed using this method.

1. ....

2. ....

(2 marks)

4   A design is going to be printed onto a batch of t-shirts.

a) **i)** Suggest a printing method that could be used.

....

(1 mark)

ii) Briefly describe this process.

....

....

(2 marks)

b)   The t-shirt design is shown in **Figure 1**. Decide whether or not this design
is suitable for the method you have chosen and explain your answer.

Figure 1

....

....

....

....

(2 marks)

Printing Quality and Finishes — 1

1   **Figure 1** shows a quality control mark used in printing.

Figure 1

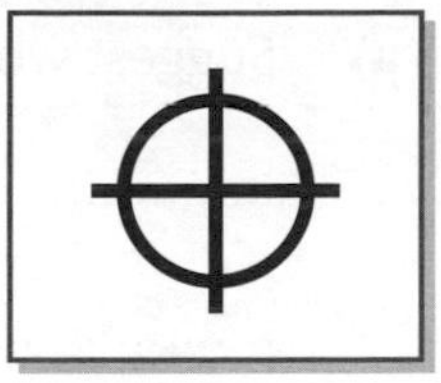

a)   **i)**   Give the name of this mark.

....
(1 mark)

ii)   Briefly describe what it is used for.

....

....
(1 mark)

b)   **i)**   Explain what crop marks are and why they are used.

....

....
(2 marks)

ii)   Explain what is meant by the 'bleed area', and say why it is used.

....

....

....
(2 marks)

c)   **i)**   Name another quality control mark used in printing.

....
(1 mark)

ii)   Describe what it is used for.

....
(1 mark)

2   Discuss the advantages and disadvantages of using **print finishes**.

....

....

....

....
(4 marks)

<u>*Printing Quality and Finishes — 2*</u>

3   Varnishing is a type of print finish used by manufacturers.

a)   Suggest why manufacturers might want to varnish a product.

....

....

(2 marks)

b)   Name **one** product that might be varnished. ....

(1 mark)

c)   Name the technique where only a small area of a product is varnished.

....

(1 mark)

4   Products made of paper and card can be laminated using plastic.

a)   Suggest **two** reasons why a product may be laminated.

1. ....

2. ....

(2 marks)

b)   Name **two** products that are often laminated.

1. ....

2. ....

(2 marks)

5   Describe what is meant by embossing and explain why it is used.

....

....

(2 marks)

6   Other than varnishing, laminating and embossing, name and briefly describe **one** other type of print finish. Give **one** example of how the finish could be used.

Print finish: ....

Description: ....

....

Use: ....

(3 marks)

Production Methods — 1

1   Templates are often used by manufacturers.

  a)   Explain what templates are used for.

  ....

  (1 mark)

  b)   Suggest **one** benefit of using a template.

  ....

  (1 mark)

2   Explain why manufacturers might choose to use **jigs** in their manufacturing processes.

Errr... wrong sort of jig.

  ....

  ....

  ....

  ....

  (3 marks)

3   Moulds are used in the manufacture of many products.

  a)   Describe what moulds are used for in manufacturing processes.

  ....

  (1 mark)

  b)   Name **two** processes that use moulds.

  1   ....

  2. ....

  (2 marks)

  c)   Give **one** advantage of using a mould in a manufacturing process.

  ....

  ....

  (2 marks)

  d)   Give **one** disadvantage of using moulds.

  ....

  ....

  (2 marks)

Production Methods — 2

4   This question is about producing a batch of products.

a)   Name the piece of equipment that can be cut around to produce identical components for a batch of products.

   ....

(1 mark)

b)   Name the piece of equipment that ensures holes are drilled in the same place in each product.

   ....

(1 mark)

5   Manufacturers try to **reduce** the **waste** produced in making their products.

a)   Give **two** reasons why manufacturers try to avoid producing too much waste.

   1.   ....

   2.   ....

(2 marks)

b)   Explain how using a design that tessellates can help to reduce waste.

   ....

   ....

(2 marks)

c)   Show that the shape in the box below will tessellate.

(2 marks)